PSALM-HYMNS

Volumes Three & Four

Psalms 73-106

Adapted by L. L. Larkins

Library of Congress Control Number:2019910383

Names: Larkins, L. L.
Title: Psalm Hymns: Volumes Three & Four, Psalms 73-106
Description: Littleton, Colorado : Capture Books, [2019] | Psalm
Hymns: Lyrics for Personal and Communal Reflection | Words only. |
Abridged. Does not include bibliographical references and index.
Identifiers: ISBN-13: 9781732445772| ISBN-10: 173244577X
| ISBN-13: 978-1-951084035 (ebook)
Subjects: LCSH: Psalms (Music) | Hymns, English, American. | Bible--
Meditations. | Worship in the Bible | Drama Anthologies
Classification: LCC BS1424 .L37 2019 | LCC BS1424 (ebook) | DDC
223/.2052--dc23
MUS052000 Music; Lyrics DRA002000 | Drama; Anthologies; Multiple
Authors

Robin Bolton, Amy Hoppes editor, Crystal Schwartzkop, editors

Psalm lyrics

for personal performance

and communal reflection

CONTENTS

Volume III (Psalms 73~89)

Volume IV (Psalm 90~106)

To the wanderers and worshipers,
to the prayers and the petulant;

May you live long, productive lives and may you prosper even as
your soul prospers.

PHOTO: CHARLENE CAWOOD

Historical Uses

Most of the book of Psalms was written in the time of David and Solomon (c. 1010–970 BC). In all Christian, Messianic and Jewish traditions, the Psalms are utilized in corporate worship, referred to in training, and for celebrations or holy day traditions. Not since the days of the Puritans, however, has there been a comprehensive and accessible psalter for singing the Psalms. Originally, Psalms 1-119 comprised the Psalter, and it is thought that the Psalms of assents were added later.

The title of the Psalms is derived from the Greek translation, ψαλμοί *psalmoi*, meaning "instrumental music" and, by extension, "the words accompanying the music."

The Psalms are to be used for drama, recitals, school choirs, songs of praise, giving thanks, and prayers in worship. The Psalms are also used for purposes of teaching theology, devotional self-editing, history, and testimony. The Puritans used the Psalms in schools to teach children many things.

For students, philosophers, and gamers, the Psalms present some interesting puzzles to solve. We see through a dim glass, but what happens to the flesh, the spirit, and the soul after death? What does it mean for believers to testify of the safety and sanctuary of God in the midst of terrorism, disease, betrayal, false witnesses, and other afflictions? What is the difference between human law, human legal processes and God's law? Who is the King so often referred to in the Psalms? Why is God called by so many different names? How does salvation through Christ converge with obedience to God's law? What does loving one's neighbors mean when confronted with some Psalm petitions to eradicate one's enemies?

The book is an anthology, part one of 150 Psalms. I have indexed the Psalms below as to their purposed use and historical interpretation.

- True Torah Piety Psalms: Psalms 1, 2, and 150.
- Psalms 20, 23, and 72 are beautiful blessings for comfort.
- Psalms of Praise include: 8, 10, 18 (and thanks), 19, 21, 24, 29, 30 (with thanks), 36, 40 (with thanks), 41, 44, 45, 46, 47, 48, 50, 65 (with thanks), 66, 67, and 68.
- Pleading Psalms include: 3, 4, 5, 6, 7, 10, 13, 17, 22, 25, 26, 28, 31, 35, 43, 54, 64, 69, 70, and 71.
- Psalms of Lament can be divided into two kinds. The first is the individual laments, many written by David. These may include personal descriptions of misery, sickness, false accusations and a plea to the sanctuary for safety, confessions and complaints and other prayers. Others are communal Psalms of mourning and suffering due to the affliction of a small group or nation.

The Lament Psalms include: 3, 4, 5, 7, 17, 26, 27, 54, 55, 57, 63, and 69. Many of these contain pleas for divine judgment and are not limited to sacred ritualistic judgments or protections from the temple or sanctuary. Some however, can be understood as a prayer written to a judge or counselor who will then take the accusations and confessions, and render judgments—after which a group would seek to be reconciled again to live in harmony. A person's small group was how a person experienced meaning and religion.

Lament is an expression of examining one's soul in the light of God's love and righteousness. It is "the discipline of self-suspicion," a term coined by the Puritan minister, Thomas Manton, in England. On August 17, 1662, Manton preached his last sermon on Hebrews 12:1 just before The Act of Uniformity led to the "Great Ejection". Without bemoaning his own demise, he sweetly exhorted his congregation, "Watch over thyself with a holy self-suspicion, because thou hast sin within thee that doth easily beset thee; therefore *consider thy ways,* Psalm 119:59; *guard thy senses,* Job 33:1; but, above all, *keep thy heart,* Proverbs 4:23. Conscience must stand porter at the door, and examine what comes in and what goes out. Watch over the stratagems of Satan, and seducing motions of thy own heart."

- o Laments involving sickness, terror, disaster or misery include: 6, 13, 22, 28, 38, and 102.
- o Community Laments do not involve significant confession. They are: 44, 60, 74, 79, 80, 83, and 89.
- o Psalms which are considered in the Anthologies of the Exiled are: 25, 33, 34, 103, 111, 112, 119, and 145.
- Psalms of the Penitent are: 6, 32, 38, 51, 102, 130, and 143.
- Over 50 Psalms were written by David and are considered to be Psalms of royalty. Followers of Jesus began assessing the Messianic relationship of these Psalms early on as relating to Christ as the Liberating King. The most significant Messianic Psalms are: 2 and 22.
- The Sons of Korah were the faithful survivors of God's judgment against their dissenting father and cohorts who were swallowed when the ground opened up. They wrote Psalms of redemption, testimony, and praise, and Psalms of lament: 42, 43, 44, 45, 46, 47, 48, and 49.
- Teaching *Maskil* Psalms include: 52, 54, and 55. Each is considered to be an advocate of enlightenment. These Psalms can, and do, teach. Each and every Psalm is educational for righteousness.

- o Psalms 11, 16, 23, 27, 46, 52, and 62 encourage us to rest in God's good sovereignty and might for safety when threatened.
- o Psalms 12, 16, and 37 compares the LORD'S friendship to the oppression of traitors and deceivers.
- o Psalms 14, 37, and 53 teaches the uselessness of fool's wisdom.
- o Psalm 15 shows that the LORD will reject slanderers, gossips and defamers from heaven.
- o Psalm 49 eloquently describes the error and foolishness of trusting in riches.
- Miktams are Psalm 16, 56, 57, 58, 59, and 60. These have a special instruction: to be performed with wind instruments or with just the voice which is a wind instrument itself. Miktam means "inscription" or "to cover." These Psalms may have to do with atonement, or because of the context of these Psalms, they may have indicated a whispered note, or, a secret note during a time of high alert or danger. They may have been a cover letter for a gift sent "under cover" i.e. Miktam (found only in books 1 & 2).

Although tunes have been chosen for each lyric, the style of how it may be sung may be as unique as each user. Try swing, or soul, or bluegrass styles besides the classic. Try dramatic readings, a cappella chorale, rock, or country. Just make a joyful noise to the LORD! Each Psalm is given space so that the musical user may add chord charts above phrases, references, musical indications, notes, or other thoughts.

BOOK THREE (PSALMS 73 - 89)

PHOTO: SHEILA DAW

PSALM 73

(A Psalm of Asaph)
Tune: IN SHADY GREEN PASTURES
(Some Through The Waters)
George A. Young, (circa 1950)

Oh, truly, God fills all of Israel with good,

   The blameless, He binds them with goodness;

But as for me, I came close to the edge

   When envy of others took hold.

      My feet were slipping, losing my way,

      Almost abandoning paths that You laid,

      I envied people of prosperous airs;

      Though they were wicked,

      they seemed without care.

Their bodies seemed healthy, so mighty and strong.

   They didn't have troubles like others; and

Never a plague known to anyone else,

   They carried their pride on their arms.

      Like a proud necklace, jewels that they'd wear,

      Clothing themselves in their opulent airs;

      Cruelly they claimed all the goodness in life,

      Scoffing at all they left

      Stalling behind.

Their boasting was heard against heavens and earth,

   Their strutting dismayed and confused us;

So drinking the poison from all of their words,

   I heard the despairing ones moan,

      "When does God listen? What does God see?"

      "Will the Most High treat their inequity?"

      Look at the wicked enjoying their ease,

      Living on interest, they're

      Playing in peace.

"Was keeping my heart pure for nothing at all?"
Regretting my trouble to stay true!
"Did I keep my innocence for a lame cause?"
For sorrow and pain wake me up!
If I had spoken this way to Your friends,
I would be labeled a traitor to them.
So to this difficult task I apply,
To comprehend why,
Only wicked preside.

Then, I went to visit My God in His place,
To visit and learn from Your presence,
And finally I understood that You give chase,
To sweep off the wicked in sin.
Truly, You put them on slippery slopes,
Sending them over the cliff without hope;
Then, in an instant, they all disappear,
The wicked completely swept
off in their fears.

When you arise, LORD, to laugh, You will laugh
    At all of their silly ideas.
You'll laugh as a person who dreams in the dawn.
    Then I'll understand I was wrong.
        My heart was bitter, perversity lied;
        I was so foolish and torn up inside.
        Ignorant, senseless, an animal wronged,
        You held my hand till
        I knew I belonged.

You guide me with counsel, You lead me along
    To destiny into full glory.
And, Whom do I have in this heaven but You?
    Your presence is all I desire!
        More than their riches, more than mystique;
        Though my health fails, though my spirit grows weak,
        God is the core and the strength of my heart;
        I belong with Him,
        And never apart.

Those who desert Him will perish by fears,

    For You will destroy those who leave You.

As for my choice, I have learned it was good;

    How good to live near to my God!

        This Sovereign LORD is the wheel of my life;

        He is my shelter, and for Him I try.

        Telling the wonderful things You have proved;

        My testimony shows

        What You can do!

PSALM 74

(A psalm of Asaph)
Tune: I NEED THEE EVERY HOUR
Robert Lowry, (1872)
Or Let There Be Peace on Earth and Let it Begin with Me

Why LORD, do You reject

Your children for so long?

Why smolder in Your wrath

And focus it on us?

Remember? Are we not the

Sheep of your own pasture?

Remember Your own people

You chose long ago!

LORD, are we not Your tribe?

You named Your special clan,

The same that You redeemed

Possessed by Your own hand!

Remember too, Jerusalem,

This, on earth, Your own home.

And, walk the awful ruins,

This city You love.

Your sanctuary ruined:
Their awful victory.
Your enemies set up
Their standard battle wings.
They shouted of their victory,
They swung their forest axes,
Like lumberjacks, they smashed up
Your sacred, carved walls.

They burned where people pray,
They burned the sacred place;
Defiled holy ground
That bears Your Holy Name.
Then like an afterthought they
Cried, "Destroy the whole thing!"
And so they burned the worshipers'
Sanctum of God.

We fail to see your signs,
Miraculous designs!
The prophets and the sage
Named after You were gone!
Can no one tell us when this
Horrid time will end here?
How long, Oh God, how long
Will You stand to the side?

How long will You endure
Our enemies defame?
How long will You allow
The mocking of Your name?
Forever, LORD, forever?
Why do You hold back Your
Own strong hand of power?
Unleash, and destroy!
Oh God, You are my King

From ages past on earth;

You bring salvation here.

You split the sea by half.

In strength, You smashed the heads of

Monsters and Leviathan.

You let the desert beasts come,

Devour, and feast.

You opened up the springs

To gush and overspill;

Then, dried up river beds

That filled our watermills.

Both day and night belong to

You, who made the starlight,

The sun and moon and boundaries of

Summer and snow!

See how these enemies

Insult and spurn Your name?

A glut of utter fools

My Lord will not arraign!

Oh, stop these beasts from gutting

The turtledoves You love, Lord!

Oh, don't forget Your suffering

People for long.

Remember faithful love's

True covenant of hope,

For, see the land is full

Of dark and violent throats!

Don't let the downtrodden

Be humiliated.

Instead, lead the afflicted

To lift up Your name!

Arise and commandeer.

Won't You defend Your cause?

Remember how the fools,

These fools, insulted God!

Now, do not overlook them

Cursing You for hours,

For they are enemies in a

Stormy uproar.

PSALM 75

(For the choir director: A psalm of Asaph)
Tune: FAITH OF OUR FATHERS, LIVING STILL
"St. Catherine," arranged by James G. Walton, (1864)
Or, Little Drummer Boy

Thank You, Oh Father,

    Because You are near;

    Thank You, Oh God, from souls everywhere!

Listen, we tell of Your wonderful deeds,

Having now glimpsed Your sovereignty.

      God is declaring, "I will plant

      Truth in its time, the provident.

"I bring the earthquake

    On those who do wrong,

    Upon the souls who stir up a throng.

I am the One keeping foundations firm.

One day I'll turn out the unconcerned.

      I warned the proud to, 'Stop your boasts!'

      I warned the wicked, 'Drop your fists!'

'Do not raise fists of

    Defiance in rants

    Against the heavens in arrogance.'"

For none on earth—from the east or the west,

None coming from the wilderness—

      Shaking their fists against our God,

      Sovereign on high, escape the Judge.

He decides each who will

    Rise and who will fall,

    Clasping a cup above, overall.

This cup is foaming with wine mixed with spice.

He pours the wine to judge every vice;

      And vile mouths must drink this cup,

      Draining it to the dregs they must.

But as for me, I will

    Always proclaim

    What God has done, and praise His name.

Singing to Jacob's God; He brings us power;

For God will break the wicked one's tower.

      "Aberrant strength is overcome,

      I will increase my godly ones."

PSALM 76

(For the choir director: A psalm of Asaph.
A song to be accompanied by stringed instruments)
Tune: BRINGING IN THE SHEAVES
(Sowing in the morning, sowing seeds of kindness)
George Minor, (1880)

God is highly honored in the land of Judah;

In the land of Israel, His name is known as Great!

Jerusalem is where our God resides in honor;

Zion is His home, the mount of saving grace.

He has broken flares, fired arrows flared,

Weapons aimed against Him, broken in midair!

You, Oh God, are glorious, evermore majestic

Than the lasting mountains filled with wild beasts.

Now their boldest warriors have been duly plundered.

Enemies are sleeping, laid before our feet!

With a blast of breath, YAHWEH's blasting breath,

God exploded chariots; horses fell in death.

Who can stand before You? I no longer wonder.

    Who can stand before You? You are greatly feared!

When Your anger visits, sentencing the prideful,

    Wiping heaven's windows, pride is fully cleared!

Making the earth quake, trembling it shakes,

Earth stood up in silence for the LORD's remake.

Here, You stand to judge, Oh God, the souls of evil,

    And to lift on high, the humble and oppressed.

God, You give us pause for human degradation,

    Serves for Your enhancement in the great redress.

All the kings observe, all the kings of earth,

Witness their dispersing, princes in reverse.

Make your vows to keep them, for the LORD accepts them.

    Honor God and bring Him, everyone, a gift.

Bring your tribute to the Awesome One Who saves you.

    For He breaks the pride of princes on the earth!

All the kings observe, all the kings of earth,

Bringing God their tribute, just as He deserves.

PSALM 77

(For the director of music. For Jeduthun. A psalm of Asaph)
Tune: WHILE SHEPHERDS WATCHED THEIR FLOCKS BY NIGHT
May also be adapted to Chestnuts Roasting on an Open Fire if the verse
breaks are ignored and the lyric sung as a long poem.

I cried out to our God for help;

    I cried out, "YAHWEH, hear me!"

In my distress, with tireless hands,

    I stretched them out for comfort;

I sought the LORD all night.

I remembered You, YAHWEH, and groaned;

    all night I meditated,

And though my fainting spirit moaned,

    You kept my eyes from closing,

Though I could find no words.

I thought of years so long ago,

    And mused on songs I sang then;

Those songs and lyrics in the night,

    That turned my heart to "A-men."

And then my spirit asked:

"Will the LORD abandon evermore?

    Will He never show His favor?

Will He hide in fog His unfailing love

    With His promises forever?

    In wrath does pardon fail?"

Then I thought, "To this I will appeal:

    The former years when the Most High

Stretched out His right compassionate hand,

    I will recall His wonders;

    Yes, I will ponder might!

Your miracles of long ago,

    Your works, I will consider

And meditate on miracles.

    Your ways, Oh God, are holy!

What god is great like You?"

You are God, whose mighty acts and deeds

    Were performed among all peoples.

You displayed Your pow'r and mighty arm

    With Your strength redeeming Jacob

With heirs of Joseph too.

The waters stood to see You, God,
  The waters watched and writhed;
The very depths convulsed not of wind.
  The clouds poured down their water,
The heavens clapped their hands!

Your arrows flashed with lightning strikes,
  And thunder was heard in the whirlwind.
 Your light lit up the world around;
  The earth, it quaked and trembled.
Your path led through the sea!

Your way led through the mighty waves,
  Though the waters held no footprints.
Where were You, God? Invisible? –
  By Your hand You led Your people,
Through Moses and Aaron.

PHOTO: SHEILA DAW

PSALM 78

(A teaching Maskil of Asaph)
Tune: ON JORDAN'S STORMY BANKS (Bound for the Promised Land)
Miss M. Durham, William Walker (New York: Hastings House, 1835);
arranged by Rigdon M. McIntosh, (1895)
It is suggested that this piece be sung with alternate tunes to relieve the
length,
or spoken, chanted, dramatically. Antiphonal choral singing
or solo leader may add interest and emphasis.
Alternate tunes: "Kingsfold," I HEARD THE VOICE OF JESUS SAY
"Forest Green," Ralph Vaughan Williams, RISE UP AND SHINE
May also be adapted to Greensleeves

My people, hear my words of teaching;

　Listen to my words.

I begin with a parable of old

　And will speak to the hidden yore, —

These are things our people have heard and known,

They are things ancestors told.

Should we try to hide them from our own

Descendants who need to know?

Telling generation next the

    Deeds the LORD has done,

Praiseworthy deeds of our own LORD,

    His power, and wonders won.

Decreeing statutes for Jacob's inheritance;

Law establishing camps.

In Israel, He commanded them

To guide their children's hands.

Tell the younger ones all these wonders and

    Tales for those to come,

So they in turn will tell these deeds

    To the next generation.

The aim of telling and not forgetting,

Do not misunderstand,

So the ages trust our sovereign God

And will keep all of His commands.

May the fearsome acts of God prevail on them

    Not to raise their fists.

Like the fists their own ancestors raised —

    In their stubborn rebelliousness.

This old generation waivered repeatedly;

Faithless to their God,

Their own souls were not stayed in faith

To Him Who is overall.

The men of Ephraim, though with armor clad,

    Turned backs from war.

On the day of battle, they refused

    To live by the law of God.

They failed to own God's sacred covenant,

They forgot His deeds,

And the wonders He had shown to them,

They renounced in their time of need.

Ancestors had told their little ones
    God's miraculous deeds,
Which they had seen performed by Him
    In the city of Zoan's reeds.
There in Egypt, the LORD divided the sea, and He
Led them through it on foot.
Yes, He made the water stand up tall
Like a wall to let them through.

He led them through the days by shrouding
    Himself in pillars of cloud.
Throughout each night He guided them
    Inside of a fiery scout.
With ease He splintered the desert rock; it
Poured them water to drink.
It streamed and flowed from rocky crags,
Abounding, enough to please.

Oh, but this generation kept on sinning and
   Putting God to the test,
Rebelling in the wilderness,
   And demanding their food, obsessed.
When they all protested this God Most High—
Presuming His power was frail,
They wailed, "Can God fill tables now,
In the wild, can He prevail?"

"Sure, He struck the rock and waters gushed
   With streams abundantly,
But can He also give us bread
   And nourish us with wheat?"
Their loud complaining arose on high to
God, whose fury hummed;
Till fire broke against the loathing of
Jacob and Israel's sons.

They did not believe in God's deliverance;

    Did not trust in Him.

Yet the skies broke up by His command,

    And He ruptured the doors of heaven.

He rained down angels' bread called manna;

They collected like wheat.

He gave them the grain of heaven's stock,

And He sent down all they could eat.

Then, He loosed the eastern wind from heaven;

    Made the south wind blow.

He rained down meat on them like sand,

    Blew in birds like on sandy shores.

The birds were falling down in their campground,

All around their tents.

They ate till they were fully gorged—

So, He yielded what they had yearned.

While this food was being chewed in their mouths;

    They ate whatever they craved;

God's anger rose against them all,

    And He put to death their brave.

Oh, the young, the strong, and the sturdiest wanderers;

God cut down these men,

For His anger kindled at the lot

Of their cravings and discontent.

Despite these wonders, they kept on blundering;

    Even with His deeds,

Not believing that God was good and great,

    Though their bodies were full of meat.

So He made life futile with years of terror,

Ending days in pain.

In their bitter years, He cut them down

For their senseless and proud disdain.

Whenever God would mow them down,
    They'd come to seek the LORD;
Returning eagerly to God,
    They remembered their Rock and core.
They recalled that God, Most High was nearby,
Their Redeemer and Friend.
Then they would flatter Him with praise,
With their lying mouths pretend.

Their hearts again would turn disloyal,
    Slack to His covenant.
Yet God was merciful again,
    Forgiving their many sins.
Their God would not destroy His children.
Holding back His wrath;
He restrained Himself time after time;
He remembered the human path.

How often they rebelled against Him

    In the wilderness,

And grieved Him in the barren land,

    Again put God to test!

Oh, Israel vexed the High and Holy One,

They forgot His hand—

The day He redeemed them from the whip—

From oppression in Egypt's land.

On the day He spread His signs in Zoan—

    Egypt's region of reeds—

His wonders turned their streams to blood;

    Their oppressors could not take a drink.

Then, He sent in swarms of flies devouring;

Frogs that poisoned their health.

He gave their crops to grasshoppers,

And to locust that ate their wealth.

Their vines, their sycamore, He destroyed them,.
    Figs were ruined with sleet.
He pelted the cattle with His hail;
    He downed their livestock meat
With bolts of lightning unleashed over them.
He shocked Egypt in wrath;
His indignation brought to them
Destroying angels' death.

The path prepared for His unleashing
    Spared no family of Ham.
In the plague, all of Egypt's firstborn died,
    For the angel took their hands.
But the Hebrew people followed Him through
Hostile wilderness;
Like a flock of sheep, He led His own.
He brought them deliverance.

As much as they were unafraid,

    Their chasers followed and sank

Into the sea engulfing them.

    Israel was saved on banks.

He brought them safe to hills that border

His good and holy land;

He drove out nations they attacked

Re-allotted their lands for them.

He settled traveling tribes of Israel

    In homes for inheritance;

 But still they put God to the test.

    There, they rebelled at Him.

They abandoned their God Most High again,

And did not keep His Word.

So they set aside His statutes there

Like their grandparents did.

Disloyal as a faulty arrow
    Faithless in their heads,
They angered God with false worship
    To idols on high instead.
And holy jealousy roused God's fury.
For with their partying sounds,
He was furious, and finally
He came down to reject His own.

He abandoned Shiloh's tabernacle,
    Left His tent with them.
He sent the ark of His own might
    To be captured away from them.
His splendor traveled to camps of enemies,
And His people died;
His inheritance made His wrath burn,
The young men died by fire.

So Israel's brides could sing no wedding songs;

    Priests were put to the sword,

And Israel's widows could not weep

    Till the Warrior awoke in God.

He awoke like awaking from a stupor of

Wine to beat his foes;

Everlasting shame He put on them,

And He crushed them with mighty blows.

Then He rejected the tents of Joseph, and

    Did not choose the tribe

Of Ephraim; but chose the tribe

    Of Judah, in Zion's Mount.

He loved them and He built His home, a

Sanctuary in heights,

Like the earth that He established here

Forever, it abides.

He chose His humble servant, David—,

    Brought him from the sheep;

Up from the pens where tending lambs

    Had taught him to rest and keep.

God made him the shepherd of His people,

All Jacob and Israel,

And David ruled with his heart,

With integrity and skill.

Psalm 79

(A psalm of Asaph)
Tune: O LITTLE TOWN OF BETHLEHEM
Lewis Redner, "St. Louis", is the tune used most often for this carol in the U.S. but in the British Commonwealth, and in the U.S. Episcopal Church, the English hymn tune "Forest Green" is used, as adapted by Ralph Vaughan Williams from an English folk ballad called "The Ploughboy's Dream"

Oh God, the nations have invaded

Your inheritance!

Throughout Your temple they've defiled, Your holy

silhouettes!

Jerusalem is rubble,

Reduced to death and shame!

They've left Your servants' bodies for the

Wild birds to claim!

They've poured out blood like water

all around Jerusalem,

And there is no one living who can bury all the dead.

    Our neighbors' taunt and scorn us;

        For their derision flies

            With those whose scorn and strong derision

            Shout on every side.

Oh, how long will Your anger last; forever,

Lord of fire?

How long, I cry, will jealousy keep burning like briar?

    Pour out Your wrath on others,

        On those preoccupied;

            On kings and nations ignorant

            Of You for all their pride.

Cull aliens to face Your name; for they've
devoured us,
Descendants and the homes of Jacob's lands, completely
crushed!
　　Do not withhold compassion
　　　　From us for ancient sins;
　　　　　　In desperate need, this generation
　　　　　　　　Begs Your great defense!

Oh help us, God our Savior, help us
glorify Your name;
Forgive our sins, atone for them, do all
this for Your sake.
　　Why should the nations prattle,
　　　　"Where is the orphans' God?"
　　　　　　Before our eyes, they'll realize
　　　　　　　　That You'll avenge our blood.

Oh, may You hear the groaning of Your own condemned
to die;
With Your strong arm preserve Your servants, give them
back their lives!
Pay back into the laps of
Our neighbors seven times
All their contempt they hurled at You,
LORD, when they scorned our lives.

Then we Your people, simple sheep, will give You
thanks Oh, LORD!
In pastures green we'll bring You praises,
Shepherd, we adore!
From generations here and
To generations there,
We will recount Your power and
Proclaim Your full repair!

PSALM 80

(For the director of music. A psalm of Asaph)

Tune: O COME, O COME EMMANUEL

"Veni Emmanuel,"15th C. plainchant: "Bone Jesu dulcis cunctis" is part
of a series of
two-part tropes to the responsory Libera me.
Alternate tunes: "St. Petersburg" by Dmitry Bortniansky, Aachen, (1841)
and "Conditor Alme Siderum"

Oh Shepherd, hear us, Shepherd of the flock!

You lead all Israel, Joseph with a rod.

   You sit enthroned between cherubim;

   You shine for Ephraim and Benjamin—

Oh God! Wake up Your mighty arm to save!

Light up Manasseh, shine for us always.

Oh God, restore us, save us LORD, for peace.

And make Your face shine on with Your increase.

   How long will You continue, we pray,

   To smolder over every prayer we say?

You feed Your own the wilted bread of tears;

We drink our bowl of sorrowing in fear.

A small thing of derision, You have made,

Our neighbors mock and enemies parade.

    Restore us, Dear Almighty, to grace;

    Your face is welcome, shine on us, embrace!

You dug us up, our vine from Egypt's ground;

You drove out others, making us abound.

You cleared the ground for transplanting this vine,

And it took root and filled the land with wine.

    The mountains then were covered with shade,

    And mighty cedars with its colonnade.

Its branches reached as far as the great Sea,

Its shoots ran to the river's apogee.

Why have You broken down supportive walls?

For strangers steal our harvest grapes in hauls.

    And from the forest, boars ravage it,

    And insects from the fields feed on its limbs.

Return to us, Almighty God to save!

Look down from heaven, watch Your vine we pray!

The root You planted with Your own right hand,

The Son, the branch, sprung of Your famous plan.

   This vine is hacked, and burned with a fire;

   At Your rebuke, Your people are a brier.

Let Your good hand rest on the man at right,

The Son of Man you raised up for Your fight.

Then we will never turn away again,

Should You revive us, we will keep Your plan.

   Restore us, LORD Almighty to save;

   Oh, make Your face shine over us again.

Oh God! You shine, You send your son to save,

So shine on us, remove us from disgrace.

PSALM 81

(For the director of music. According to *gittith.* Of Asaph)
Tune: WE THREE KINGS OF ORIENT ARE
John Henry Hopkins, Jr., for the General Theological Seminary
(New York City, 1857)

Sing for joy to YAHWEH our strength;

   Shout to Jacob's God and sing!

Start the music, strike the timbrel,

Playing the harp and strings. Oh-oh—

     Sound the shofar on that day

     When the new moon finds its sway;

     And the festival should bring in,

     All our gladness on display!

This is a decree to observe,

   This, the ordinance of our God,

God of Israel, God of Jacob,

After He fought for you. Oh-oh—

     God established this new rule,

     When against Egyptians blew;

     As for Joseph, his descendants

     Celebrate the one true God.

Then, I heard an unknown voice:

   "I removed the weight that was hoist

On their shoulders, from their shoulders;

So I set free their hands. Oh-oh—

     They were freed from overloads,

     From their quota, from their ropes.

     When you called on Me, then I listened;

     Then I saved in thunder-shows!"

"At the bitters of Meribah,

   There, I tested you for My awe.

Hear my warning, all my people,—

Only listen now! Oh-oh—

     Never take a foreign god

     In among you, don't applaud.

     Do not worship any other;

     I alone Am God, your God."

"Now, forever, I Am your God,

　Freed from Egypt, I brought you up.

Open wide your mouth, I'll fill it.

Open wide your mouth! Oh-oh—

　　But My people closed their ears—

　　Would not listen, would not hear.

　　Israel would not, would not, would not!

　　They would not come near to hear."

"When I saw they meant their goodbye,

　Then I gave them over to lies,

Then they followed their contrivances,

Making faulty wiles. Oh-oh—

　　If My people only came

　　Near to Me to hear again,

　　Oh, if only Israel followed,

　　For My better way is plain!"

"See how quickly I would subdue

   All oppressors over you,

Turn My hand against your enemies,

All who would hate the Lord! Oh-oh—

    They would cringe before My hand,

    Yet their punishment would stand.

    You, beloved, I would feed you

    Honey wheat from finest lands."

PSALM 82

(A prophetic psalm of Asaph)
Tune: BATTLE HYMN OF THE REPUBLIC
from "John Brown's Body" a United States folk and marching tune.

Standing in the great assembly,

God presides and takes His place;

He is rendering His judgment

To the gods of earth's dismay.

His decree begins by reasoning:

"How long have you displaced

The weak and fatherless?"

God presides to judge the jurists;

Earth is trembling in her footsteps;

God inherits all the nations.

Our God is over all!

"Why do you defend the wicked

who show partiality?

Will you not defend the weak and save

The destitute who weep?

Will you not uphold the cause of all

The poor and the oppressed?

For nations belong to God."

God presides to judge the jurists;

Earth is trembling in her footsteps;

God inherits all the nations.

Our God is over all!

'Will you rescue and deliver

Weak and needy from the hands

Of the wicked and perverse who keep

Oppression in their lands?

With their lack of understanding,

Little gods know little plans;

They walk in shades of dark."

God presides to judge the jurists;

Earth is trembling in her footsteps;

God inherits all the nations.

Our God is over all!

I attributed to jurists

and the kings who did preside,

"You are 'gods, the sons of Father God,

Commander, Judge on High.'

But the Judge decrees that you are mortal,

felled like every son.'"

For nations belong to God.

God presides to judge the jurists;

Earth is trembling in her footsteps;

God inherits all the nations.

Our God is over all!

PSALM 83

(A psalm of Alarm by Asaph)
Tune: O COME, ALL YE FAITHFUL
Adeste Fideles, uncertain. Possibly John Reading (c. 1645–1692) or
King John IV of Portugal (c. 1650) or John Francis Wade (1711–1786)
who signed and published it.

Oh, do not keep silent, God, do not keep silent!

Oh, do not resolve to hold Your peace, Highest God!

Do You hear the uproar that Your foes are making?

They raise their heads against You;

They lay their crafty plans out

Against Your hidden people; they're plotting as one.

They say, "Come together, let us wipe them all out:

The Nation of Israel be remembered no more!"

The tent homes of Edom make their covenant with

The Ishmaelites and Moab,

The Hagrites and Philistia

With Amalek and Ammon, and Assur and Lot.

So do to these nations as You did to Midian,

To Sis'ra and Jabin at the banks of Kishon.

For they became dung for fertilizing Endor.

Oh, make their nobles like them:

The princes of Zalmunna

And Oreb, Zeeb and Zebah who've ruined Your lands.

My God, turn the raiders, claiming God's good homelands,

To stubble and tumbleweeds in twirling winds.

Consume them with fire, in the woods and mountains.

May You pursue their lot with

A blazing flame and tempest,

And terrify the lot with Your hurricane!

Pour shame on their image, as they turn to view You,

In shame, may they see Your name in banners, Oh Lord.

Let foes be dismayed and perishing forever;

Let their disgrace be telling

That You are Most Compelling;

They rose against the Lord, Whose name is over the earth.

PSALM 84

Tune: JOYFUL, JOYFUL, WE ADORE THEE
"Hymn to Joy," from the 9th Symphony of Ludwig van Beethoven,
(1824); adapted by Edward Hodges,
Alternate Tune: I WILL SING THE WONDROUS STORY OF THE
CHRIST OF CALVARY, Hyfrydol,
by Rowland H. Prichard (1830) And Chestnuts Roasting on an Open Fire

Oh, how lovely is Your Temple,

Splendid King, resplendent LORD!

And I long, yes, faint with longing,

For a footstep near Your courts.

See I am coming into His courtyard,

By the Living God, received;

Even swallows and young sparrows

Nest in welcome, nest in peace.

Here among Your holy altars—

There they nest and have their young,

Commandeering Angel armies.

You're my King, and You're my God!

Listen, hear the happy birdsong;

They accompany Your praise!

With the ones who live in worship,

Altogether, songs they raise.

Oh, how happy are the strong ones

Of the LORD, who walk with You,
Those who want beyond temptations
To be true and follow through.
When they walk through Rifts of Weeping,
Ancient springs become their rest;
In transforming pools of blessing,
Rains collected to refresh!

In their rectitude of strength, they
Come to meet our Mercy Shield:
He's the LORD in Zion's high court;
Our Defender and our Seal.
You are YAHWEH, the Almighty!
Oh, Most High, so near and fair!
Listen to Your own Anointed,
Israel's God, let all take care!

Show Your kindness, Your compassion,

For Your mercy covers shame.

And a single day in worship

Betters any thousand days!

I would rather be a doorman

For the worshipers of God

Than to live in gaudy mansions,

And wherever You are not.

See the Light of YAHWEH's brilliance,

Like the sun and like a shield,

He Protects our steady passage;

He provides exquisite fields.

No good thing is He withholding

From all those who walk His path!

This, the LORD of angel armies,

Shelters those of truthfulness.

PSALM 85

(For the Director of Music, Thoughts of the Sons of Korah)
Tune: AMAZING GRACE
Unknown. "New Britain" (1835)
May be adapted to Little Drummer Boy

Oh LORD, You've shown Your pleasure here,

Your land and wealth restored!

With Jacob's good repute and joy,

Our sins have been transferred!

You set aside Your wrath in full,

And turned from fierce intent,

Restoring us, our Savior God,

Erasing our offense!

Shall judgment run forever strong?

Shall generations waste?

You shall revive us once again

So let Your people praise!

Lord, show unfailing love to us;
Oh, grant salvation true!
I'll bear Your peace and serve in faith,
For God is all virtue.

He promised peace to all His own,
His faithful servants raised!
Oh, keep them from their foolish ways,
All those whom reverence saved.

So generations rest in God,
While Love and Faith lock hands.
When Peace and Right embrace and kiss,
His glory shares our land!

True faith springs from the barren earth,
The just look down from heav'n.
We've learned the Lord gives good always,
For Eden thrives again.

He leads with honesty ahead;

His feet prepare the way;

He steps in right, in good, in peace;

We follow and obey.

PHOTO: CHARLENE CAWOOD

PSALM 86

(A prayer of David)

Tune: I SURRENDER ALL (ALL TO JESUS I SURRENDER)

Winfield S. Weeden (1896)

Hear my plea, LORD, answer me now;

   I am poor, and needy, too.

Guard my life, for I am faithful;

   Save the one who trusts in You.

Bring, Almighty God,

Mercy for this child!

LORD, all day to You I'm pleading:

Make me reconciled.

LORD, I know You're good and loving,

   All-forgiving when You're called.

Hear my prayer, LORD;

   Listen closely,

I'm distressed and downward sprawled.

There is none like You!

God, with all You do:

Acts of kindness, sweet resilience,

Mercies through and through!

All the nations You created,

    By and by will worship You;

They will bring tribute to glory,

    To Your name and great virtue.

You are God alone!

How Your deeds are known!

Great and marvelous in wisdom—

You, and You alone.

Teach me, Lord, Your faithful pathways.

    May I fully lean on You;

May my heart be undivided,

    That I reverence only truth.

I will praise Your name!

God, with all my heart!

And forever, may I bring You

Glory and regard.

For Your love is great towards me;

    You delivered me from death,

Prideful foes attacked Your servant,

    Ruthless people take my breath!—

No regard for You.

Yet my gracious God,

Great in mercy, slow to anger,

Surging faithful love!

Turn Your heart to me in mercy;

    Show Your strength on my behalf;

Save me, like You saved my mother,

    I am walking in her path.

Send a sacred sign,

Goodness here define;

Hateful ones will see Your helpful

Comforts of design.

PSALM 87

(A psalm of the Sons of Korah to be sung)
Tune: GLORIOUS THINGS OF THEE ARE SPOKEN
"Austria," by Franz J. Haydn (1797),
possibly from a Croatian folk melody

He has founded His great city

On the holy mountain of God.

The LORD loves the gates of Zion,

More than Jacob's other lofts.

Glorious things are said of You, oh,

City of our God and King:

"I'm recording now, Rahab-Egypt

And Babylon for they acknowledged Me.

They believed Me — I made note of it,

Tyre and Philistia too;

They, along with Cush for Nile —

I transferred their birth to You."

Indeed, it will be said of Zion,

"This and that one here were born,

And the Most High will establish her."

The LORD God will make the word transfer.

He will write their names as citizens

In the register of births

Of His people born in Zion:

"Add this one to Zion's worth."

They will make new music singing, "All my

fountains are in You."

And the Most High will establish her.

The Lord God Himself will make this occur.

PSALM 88

(A song. A psalm of the Sons of Korah. For the director of
music. According to *mahalath leannoth,*
this is *a* teaching *Maskil* of Heman the Ezrahite)
Tune: LORD, PLANT MY FEET ON HIGHER GROUND
(I'm Pressing on the Upward Way.)

You are my LORD, the God who saves;

    You rescue when I cry in faith.

Oh, hear another prayer to You;

    Oh, turn toward my anguished soul.

I'm overwhelmed with troubles, LORD;

    See how my breath in whispers pours.

They've counted me among the dead;

    And lacking strength, my friends have fled.

You have me in the darkest depths,
    the lowest slit, will You forget?
Your wrath exterminates my life;
    In overwhelming waves I die.
You isolate me from my friends,
    And made me horrible to them;
For I'm confined. I can't escape;
    My sight is dimming in dismay.

I call lamenting every day;
    I spread my hands to You and pray.
Do You show wonders to the dead?
    Do spirits rise to praise instead?
Do You declare a faithful home
    To those impaired by Sheol's clothes?
Are wonders known in that dark place,
    And are Your righteous deeds awake?

The land of ruin is not for me.

    I wake and wrestle in my sleep.

In morning hours You'll hear my prayer.

    Why, Lord, do You forget my care?

Why do You hide Your face of love?

    In times of youth I suffered much,

And I have borne my fright and fear;

But now I'm pleading in despair.

Your wrath has swept my days like sand;

    My fear of You destroys my stand.

For dread arises like a flood,

    And all day long I am engulfed.

    You have removed my closest friend,

    And casual neighbors, You suspend.

The closing darkness hovers by—

This sunless neighbor, and I cry.

PSALM 89

(A *maskil* of Ethan the Ezrahite for recitation or singing)
Tune: I WILL SING OF THE MERCIES OF THE LORD FOREVER
James Henry Fillmore (circa. 1930)

I will sing of the mercies of the LORD

Forever;

   I will sing, I will sing!

For Your great love is faithful; it will last

Forever,

And my mouth will declare it in a song!

   As my legacy of trust,

   I will declare Your standing love:

   The breadth and faithfulness heights of it,

   Fill heaven with Your faithful covenant!

For You said, "I have sworn to David,

He's My servant,

And My Own Chosen One

Will come through him."

Praising all of Your wonders, Lord, they

Fill the heavens;

   And on earth, You are known;

For in every assembly of the

Holy body,

They are lifting Your faithfulness as one.

   "Who is like the Lord on high?

    The skies above are not as rare!

    Who compares among the heavenly beings?

    Yahweh is revered in holy councils."

All the holy ones of God

Say He is awesome

Over all who surround

This Mighty King!

All Your might and Your faithfulness surround
You always;

    It surpasses surging seas.

When the waves mount in heights of terror, You
Bring silence.

For You crush insolence to ocean sprees;

    With Your shofar and Your strength,

    You've scattered these Your enemies.

    All the heav'ns belong to You Oh, Lord,

    The earth and all the world found within it!

You created the north and south;

Your arm is power;

Peaks of Hermon and Tabor
Sing Your name.

Your strong hand is endowed with power, and
Exalted;
 Cornerstones of Your throne
Are foundations of Righteousness and
Justice only
While Your love and Your faithfulness go on.
 Blessed are the ones You train,
 Who learn of You and Your acclaim,
 Those who walk in holy radiance,
 For LORD, in Your presence is happiness!
All day long they rejoice because
Your name is fitting;
You Are all, and they
Celebrate Your Right.

For our own source of glory and our strength

Comes only

Through the horn of the Lord.

By Your favor, You lift our sphere and

Scope of power;

Yes, our shield and our sovereignty is Yours.

You're our King, the Holy One

Of Israel, of Israel.

Once, You spoke within a dream,

To give to all the faithful supreme hope:

"I have given a grace and strength

To one young warrior;

I have raised David up

Among his own.

I selected a sacred oil for

Anointing

    The young son I sustain:

For My hand will uphold him and My arm

Will strengthen,

That no wicked oppression will profane.

    Enemies will never better him;

    For, I will crush all counterclaims;

    I will strike all those opposing him.

    My faithful love embraces him always!

And because of My name,

His arm is influential.

I will give David

Rivers and the sea.

He will call out to Me in prayer, 'You are

my Father,

    And my Rock, Savior, God.'

He's appointed above the rest to

Be My heir,

To be the king most exalted on the earth.

    I maintain My love in faithfulness

    To this My son, and royal line,

    My covenant is intertwined,

    For now He is established forever!

David's throne will endure as

Long as there are heavens,

Even when David's sons

Forsake My law.

If his sons wander off from My commands

And statutes,

    If they breach My decrees,

I will punish their sinning with a rod for flogging,

But I'll

Not turn away his royalty.

      I will not remove My son,

      My promises in faithfulness.

      I will never violate My love,

      Or alter My covenant's purpose.

Once for all, I have sworn by

My own holy purchase—

I will never abandon

David's line.—

David's line will continue for My
Present glory,

    And his throne like the sun;
It will be established like the
Moon, forever,
As the unfailing witness in the sky."'

    David's line will now complain:

    "Oh, haven't You become untrue?

    In Your anger, You were shrewd to him,

    Renouncing Your oaths to Your servant!
You have spurned the anointed one
To which Your covenant was made,
Haven't You
Removed his crown?

You have broken his walls and laid his

Royalty in dust,

    Defiled of the ground;

And reduced David's strongholds

Into plunder,

For all those who scorn him and all his renown.

    You have lifted up triumphantly,

    The heavy hand of David's foes;

    You have made his every enemy

    Rejoice as though they'd trampled his train and gown.

Yes indeed, You have double cut

Your own to pieces,

And have not given aid

In time of war.

You have chased David's splendor to the end,
And cast his

    Youthfulness to the ground;
Then, You covered his body with a
Shameful mantle.
So, how long, Lord, will all of this go on?

    Will you hide Yourself forever?

    How long will anger burn like fire?

    Oh, remember my mortality,

    For all of this is futile humanity!
Who can live in creation, and not
Shirk death's power,
Or escape reclamation
Of the grave?

Where is Your former love? Oh LORD, restore

Its greatness

    By Your sworn faithfulness,

Covenanted to David; yet we see

Your servant

Mocked and beaten, my heart can bear no more!

    Hear the taunts of nations' surges,

    The scorn of all their hatefulness,

    They have mocked Your finest servant, LORD,

    And they stalk anointed steps of the Holy One.

Bring all praise to the LORD forever!

Praise the holy high

Command, with agreement

And A-men."

~BOOK FOUR (PSALMS 90 - 106)~

PHOTO: SASHA SAUR

PSALM 90

(A prayer of Moses the man of God.)
Tune: DOXOLOGY (Praise God from Whom All Blessings Flow)
Old Hundredth, Loys "Louis" Bourgeois (1630)
May be adapted to Oh, Come, Oh, Come Emmanuel or Breath of Heaven

LORD, You have been our dwelling place,

   Through generations, faithful grace;

Before the mountain peaks could rise,

   Before You formed the earth and skies!

From everlasting, God, not born,

   To everlasting, You are God!

You breathe, returning life to dust,

   And by Your word, return we must.

A thousand years are like a day,

   They're passing by beneath Your gaze.

A midnight watch is marking stride,

   and mortal souls are swept aside.

In morning's gilded light, all souls

   Shine full and bright til evening tolls.

So easily each soul will wilt,

   So terrified are souls in guilt.

You bring to light our prideful bent,
    Exposing secrets to dispense.
Our days pass under righteousness;
    We finish up our years in ash.

Our days may come, if strength endures,
    To seventy or eighty years;
yet in the best of them we know,
    Trouble and sorrow here below.

Days quickly pass, and on we fly.
    If only we had recognized.
Your will withheld what was our due,
    Since we live without fear of You.

Teach us to number all our days,
    That we may gain a heart of praise,
from loving wisdom, this You grant.
    In Your compassion, LORD, relent!

How long, Oh Lord, will You be long?

   Your servants long to find their home!

Oh fill our want in morning love;

   Grant us, Oh Lord, unfailing love!

That we may sing for joy, be glad

   In just as many days were sad.

Make us to know Your pleasing deeds;

   Array Your splendor, there proceed.

Establish all our masterwork;

   May You establish every berth,

And Your delight in beauty rest

   Upon us, every soul be blessed— A-men!

PSALM 91

(God's Protection from a Viral Plague)
Tune: THERE'S ROOM AT THE CROSS FOR YOU
By Ira F. Stamphill (1946)

The one who lives under His shield,

in protection of God, the Most High,

securely is sealed

in the Almighty's shade.

And, this is the reason I rest unafraid:

"Oh LORD, in Your home concealed,

I can rest from my battle field."

Oh, find Him today,

And He'll keep you safe

from the plague and from those who prey!

He drapes you with pinions of care;

His feathers— your cover, your shield.

He will lift from despair.

And, true to His Word,

He closes the gates on contagions that surge;

The terrors of night are sealed.

The arrows of day, repealed.

The plague in the dark,

That fells many hearts —

Yet, our God is your saving rock!

You'll witness the sentence conveyed;

You'll see how the wicked are spilled.

But because you have made

The LORD your stockade;

The Most High will hide you in His barricade.

Into your lament, no harm,

No plague to your tent will come.

For angels obey,

His goodwill conveyed.

He will shield you in all your ways.

Supporting you with angel hands

That your soul does not trip on a stone.

As a scion, you'll stand

On the lion and snake;

For He is devoted to Me for My sake,

I'll carry him from his pain;

Because he asserts My name.

In the day when he calls

No harm will befall;

I am nearby and overall.

My hand of Salvation controls

Rewarding the trusting who call;

I will make him go on,

Delivered and strong,

I'll rescue and honor the faithful one.

For I answer your love with life,

Acknowledge Me day and night!

Then, I'll show you My light,

Salvation's full might,

My presence and My delight.

PSALM 92

(A psalm for the day of rest, or Sabbath)
Tune: HE HIDETH MY SOUL
(A WONDERFUL SAVIOR IS JESUS MY LORD)
William J. Kirkpatrick (1890)

Your goodness, O God,

Makes me praise You much more,

Attuned to Your name, O Most High;

Proclaiming at all times, You carry out love

In faithfulness, morning and night!

Now, whoever hears of our musing with strings,

Will understand how glad we are.

In melodies, hearing the joy that You bring;

Your deeds, they will now understand.

How great are the works of Your hand!

Profound are Your thoughts,

LORD, the senseless can't know,

And fools do not quite comprehend;

Though evil grows wild like the prairie to seed,

The wicked will soon meet their end.

For You, LORD, are true and exalted in power.

All enemies cower Your scythe.

For You, LORD, are just to destroy the unjust,

And punish the wicked by right;

You banish the vile from sight.

My strength, LORD,

You lift it so rugged and true;

Anointing my head with fine oil.

I've heard You come routing iniquity's voice!

I've watched their defeat in the spoil.

The sap of the saints bearing fruit like a palm,

The righteous are thriving and green;

Transplanted so young to the house of the LORD,

In courts of our God they declare

That He is our rock, true and fair.

The righteous will flourish

Like palms in the sun,

As Lebanon cedars, they grow.

The leaves staying green in the courts of the LORD,

And bearing good fruit as they go,

Inside the LORD's house, they will call with delight.

"The LORD is upright!" They will sing.

No malice or fraud can be found in the LORD.

No wickedness, shadows, or sting,

The LORD is our rock and our King.

PSALM 93

(A Royal Psalm)
Tune: JOY TO THE WORLD!
First published in 1719 in Isaac Watts' English collection;
The Psalms of David, though the tune was first applied to Ps. 98

Our LORD is robed in majesty;

The LORD is armed with strength!

Enthroned, He is reigning –

Eternally, He's reigning –

The world lies in His hand,

The world lies in His hand,

Established, from long ago,

Securely held.

O, hear the seas lift up their voice,

O, LORD, the ocean's voice!

Their mightiness has frightened us.

Yet, mightier on high is this,

The thunder of His might,

The thunder of His might,

More mighty than breakers—

The LORD on high!

See, Your statutes, Lord, stand firm;
 Your statutes, Lord, stand firm!
They decorate Your house and home
Uniquely, they adorn Your throne.
 The world lies in Your hand,
 The world lies in Your hand,
 Established, from long ago,
 Securely held.

PSALM 94

(A Declaration to God and to Fools)
Tune: I WONDER AS I WANDER
John Jacob Niles (1933)
Alternate Tunes: IMMORTAL, INVISIBLE GOD ONLY WISE
Orig. St. Denio, Welsh melody, from Canaidau y Cyssegr,
by John Roberts (1839)
AWAY IN A MANGER
Mueller, James R. Murray (1887)

The LORD is a God who avenges His own.

    Oh, God my avenger, appear and shine on!

Rise up, Judge of earth's haughty; rise and repay

The lot they deserve, LORD, how long till that day?

The wicked are jubilant, arrogant rogues;

    How long will they pour out their arrogant words?

The doers of evil are boasting their game.

They're crushing Your people, LORD; widows are slain!

They murder the fatherless, press the poor,

    Run through Your inheritance, saying, "The LORD

Is taking no notice, our God does not see."

Take notice, you foolish ones! Look now, and see!

You, fools among people; you fools should wise up!

 Does He who has fashioned your ears not hear much?

Does He who forms eyes and designs not see true?

Does He punish nations and not punish you?

Does this One, who teaches man, lack any thought?

 The LORD knows the plans you make all come to naught;

How blessed the one whom You discipline, LORD,

How blessed the one whom You teach from your law!

You grant us relief from the troubles we're thrown,

 The LORD won't reject or abandon His own;

Till a pit is dug for the wicked to lay,

He'll never abandon His righteous ones' day.

Take courage for judgment will soon run upright,

 and all who believe it are also upright.

Oh, who will rise up for me against the vile?

Oh, who will stand and pledge against their guile?

Unless the Lord had provided me help,

    I soon would have ended in silence of death.

But When I admitted, "My footstep has slipped,"

Your unfailing love, Lord, supported me then.

When cares were abounding, Lord, You brought me joy.

    When anxious, Your great consolation deployed!

But, how can a throne so corrupt be allied

with You— for this throne brings despair codified?

They banded together against righteous ones,

    Condemning the innocent till they succumbed.

The Lord has become my fort and my rescue.

And I hide in God for the rock of refuge.

Oh, He will repay evildoers for sins;

    And He will destroy them for their wickedness.

The Lord will destroy them, for He is our God.

My confidence rests in the cleft of the Rock.

PSALM 95

(A Royal Psalm – A Call to Worship)
Tune: O, HOLY NIGHT
Adolphe Adams (1847)

Come, let us shout; make joyful noise to our LORD;

In triumph, shout to our refuge and rock!

Come, let us enter His presence with thanksgiving;

And let us shout to Him in a victor's song.

The LORD is a great God, above all rulers!

All the depths of earth are in His hand;

All mountain peaks are His, He made them rise up.

The sea is His; for He formed it with His hands;

O, come, let us worship our Maker and bow down.

We kneel before the LORD our God, our Maker;

We are the sheep and the people of His hand.

If you can hear, His voice today is calling;

"Do not repeat hardened hearts at Meribah.

As on that day at Massah, in the wild;

Where your ancestors tested Me and tried;

Though they had seen the wonders that I did there.

Then, I despised those hearts for forty years;

They never entered My rest in all their years.

Then, I despised those hearts that went astray.

I swore in My anger, 'They do not know My ways.'

I swore in My anger, 'They do not know My ways.'"

PSALM 96

(A Royal Psalm – A Call to Worship and Praise)
Tune: I SAW THREE SHIPS
Arr. of *Greensleeves*, 17th century, possibly Derbyshire,
also published by William Sandys in 1833

O, sing a novel song to God;

　　Proclaim His name, proclaim His name!

Come all the earth to praise the LORD;

For saving grace every morning!

Praise the LORD, His saving name;

　　Declare his deeds, declare his deeds!

His glory through all nations,

And all the races wonder!

The LORD is great and greatly feared,

　　Above all gods, above all gods!

Our God is worthy of our praise;

Above the nations' idols!

LORD made every heaven,

   In splendor, in splendor!

Before Him, strength and majesty,

In sanctuary of glory.

Ascribe to God, the families

   Of nations, of nations!

The strength and glory due His name;

Ascribe, and bring an offering!

O, come into His courts with fear;

   O, worship Him, O, worship Him!

The LORD in Holy splendor;

And tremble, all of the earth!

Proclaim among the nations:

   "The LORD reigns, the LORD reigns!"

The world is firmly set in stone;

And it shall never be toppled!

The LORD will judge humanity
  With equity, with equity!
Oh, let the earth be glad to sing;
And heavens filled with rejoicing!

Let all the sea resound in song,
  And all within, and all within!
And, let the fields be jubilant,
And everything within them!

Let all the trees rejoice and praise;
  The forests sing, the forests sing!
Let all creation now rejoice
Before the LORD who is coming!

He comes to judge the earth complete
  In righteousness, in righteousness!
So, He will judge humanity
In faithfulness the world-wide!

PSALM 97

(A Royal Psalm)

TUNE: I KNOW WHOM I HAVE BELIEVED
(I Know Not Why God's Wondrous Grace To Me He Hath Made
Known)
James McGranahan (1883)

The LORD, He reigns, let the earth be glad;

    Let distant shores rejoice.

Thick clouds intensify and cover Him;

    And fire is His ploy.

        Righteousness is

        The founding cornerstone

        Of the LORD'S reigning throne.

        And Justice is His home.

        He is stepping

        As fire goes before,

        Lightning combs the world around!

Consuming enemies on every side,

  The earth is trembling to see.

Like wax, the mountains melt before the LORD,

  For all the living to perceive.

      Now the heavens

      Proclaim His righteousness.

      As every eye attests,

      His glory manifests.

      All who worship

      Another idol's fame,

      And their images are shamed!

O, bow to worship God, you lesser gods!

    For Zion celebrates to hear

That Judah's villages are blessed and glad.

    For judgments, everyone is clear.

        Over all earth,

        You are the LORD, Most High!

        You are exalted far

        Above all other gods.

        Those who love You

        Despise the evil, LORD,

        For You guard Your faithful ones!

He guards posterity of faithful ones,
    Delivers from the evil hand
Of wicked powers and of smaller gods,
    And idols covering the land.
        Light is sown in
        The righteous, shining on;
        And joy is budding in
        Every upright stand.
        O, rejoice in
        The LORD, you righteous ones,
        We will praise His Holy Name!

PSALM 98

(A Royal Psalm – A Call to Rejoice in God's Faithful, Righteous Judgment)
Tune: THE HOLLY AND THE IVY
collected by Cecil Sharp, by Mary Clayton of Chipping Campden (1909)
or French carol: Il Est Ne (He is Born)
Or, French Carol: Entre le bœuf et l'âne gris (Between the Ox and Gray Donkey)
Or, His Eye is On the Sparrow and I Know He's Watching Me

Sing to the LORD a new song,

The marvels He has done;

His right hand, His holy arm

Have worked His salvation.

The LORD designed salvation,

He's known to every land;

Revealing righteousness to us,

To the world and all nations.

He has remembered Israel
   With faithfulness and love;
All inhabitants on earth have seen
   The salvation of our God.

Shout in your joy to YAHWEH!
   May all the earth be glad,
Bursting into Jubal's song of praise,
   Making music to the LORD.

Now with the harp and singing,
   With trumpets blasting rings;
The bellows of the ram's horn—
   Shout for joy before this King.

The seas resound like big bands,
   Drumming everything to sand;
With the world, and all who live in it.
   Let the rivers clap their hands.

Let the mountains sing together;

    Sing with joy before the LORD,

For He comes to judge the world's decrees.

    His righteousness restore.

The LORD will judge all races,

    Not with sleight of hand or bribe,

Not with human minds or human laws,

    But with fairness He decides.

PSALM 99

(A Royal Psalm)
Tune: I WILL SING OF MY REDEEMER,
(and His Wondrous Love for Me)
(Sing, O Sing) Burnley James McGranahan (1877)
Alternate tune: TIS SO SWEET TO TRUST IN JESUS
William James Kirkpatrick (1838-1921)
Hyfrydol, Rowland H. Prichard (1830)
STAND BY ME Hymn by Charles Tindley (1905)

Let all the nations

    Hear the LORD reigns,

Let them tremble for His throne;

Sitting, robed by cherubim, O,

Let the earth shake

    For His throne.

        Great in Zion, let them praise Him,

        For He is the Holy One.

        LORD, exalted over the nations,

        Let them praise You, Awesome One!

Listen, for the

    Just and mighty;

For the King is made complete.

You've established equity; and

Jacob's welfare for

    His seed.

        We exalt the LORD our God, and

        At His feet, we worship Him;

        He is Holy. He is Awesome.

        Let us praise amazing deeds!

Moses and his

    Brother, Aaron,

Called the LORD GOD's saving name;

Little Samuel called the LORD, too.

From the cloud,

    He answered them.

        These are examples of His priesthood:

        Keeping the statutes and the decrees

        That He gave them, for He loved them,

        For their welfare and their peace.

Though You punished

    Their misdeeds, You

Answered Israel with Your peace.

How forgiving and restoring,

We exalt our

    God and Chief!

        At His holy mountain of worship,

        We will bow to worship Him.

        He avenges all the wrongs done

        To His people, and defends.

PSALM 100

(A psalm for giving grateful praise.)
Tune: THE LORD OF THE DANCE
(I Danced In The Morning When The World Was Begun)
American Shaker song "Simple Gifts", and the song "The Crow on
the Cradle"

Let's shout to the LORD, for joy all the earth.

  O, worship Him in mindful mirth;

Let's answer the LORD with our joyful songs

Till we know, till we know that the LORD is God!

  He is the LORD who formed

  Life and our bodies before we were born,

  And we're made for Him, we know His voice

  We are His, we are His, His sheep of choice!

Now, enter His gates with thanksgiving and praise

  O, enter His courts to celebrate His name;

For the LORD is good, His love endures!

Forever His faithfulness has stood!

  Through all good and bad,

  Our shepherd will guide, we're glad, we're glad.

  Throughout all time and generations,

  Our LORD leads on, our LORD leads on!

PSALM 101

Tune: TIS SO SWEET TO TRUST IN JESUS
William James Kirkpatrick (1838-1921)
AlternateTune: I Will Sing of My Redeemer*(Sing, O Sing)*
Burnley James McGranahan (1877)

I will sing your love and justice;

Lord, to you, I will sing praise.

Careful, blameless, I will lead a

Life that longs for You to save!

When will You come, LORD, to visit;

See my blameless, trusting heart?

I won't seek for man's approval

Of my house or for my part.

What the faithless do, I hate, here;

I will have no part in it.

I'll avoid deceitful thinking;

I will have no counterfeit.

Those who in secret slander neighbors,

I will silence maddening lies;

Those with proud and haughty eyes, I

Will not tolerate their pride.

I will focus on the faithful
In the LORD, they dwell with me;
Those who mentor and encourage
Those who walk in purity.

Those who practice their deceit will
Never dwell within my house;
Never one with false discussions -
Silencing what they espouse.

Every morning I will silence
All the wicked in the land;
Shutting doors on evildoers
In His City, so we'll stand.

PSALM 102

(A prayer of an afflicted person who has grown weak and pours out
a lament before the LORD.)
Tune: THE GOD OF ABRAHAM PRAISE
(Geistliche Kirchengesanger Cologne)
Thomas Olivers (1772) based on the Jewish hymn, Yigdal
Alternate Tune: Crown Him with Many Crowns
DIADEMATA by George J. Elvey (1868)
Some verses may also be adapted to The Holly and the Ivy

O, hear my prayer, today;

LORD; let my cry be heard,

  And do not hide Your face from me

    In my distress!

O, turn your ear to me and quickly answer, now.

My soul is vanishing like smoke,

My flesh is death.

The edges of my heart

Are blighted like the grass;

  I wilt for I forget to eat

    In my distress!

I groan, I am reduced to skin and bone on fire;

My flesh is like a desert owl,

In ruins, perplexed.

I lie awake at night;

I have become a bird,

   A bird upon a rooftop,

      Taunted by my fears.

For those against me rail, they use my name to curse.

And I eat ashes as my food

And drink my tears.

Because of Your great wrath,

You've snatched me up and tossed.

   My days are thrown like shadows; I am

      Withered like grass.

But You, O Lord, will reign, forever more You live;

Your own renown endures throughout

All eras, fast.

Display compassion now!

For Zion's time has come!

   Appointed, You will rise to favor,

      Blessing Your own;

Your servants, like Yourself, hold dear the stones of Zion;

Her very dust moves them to pity,

Blessed home.

The nations soon will fear

The power of Your name;

    All kings of earth will soon revere

       Your glorious strength.

For He rebuilds the site, and He will not despise.

He will respond to every prayer of

Stricken cries.

Let this be written down

For people not yet born;

    That they may praise the Lord

      On high, adoring His name:

"The Lord looked down to hear the rising of prisoner's cries

From heaven's door, He viewed the earth and

Their demise.

The purpose of the Lord

Releases those condemned."

    So our Lord's name will be declared

      In Zion's praise.

Jerusalem, with those forever He has claimed,

His kingdom will assemble to

Extol His name.

My life will testify;

His power broke my strength.

    The LORD cut short my days on earth

        And, I felt robbed:

"YAHWEH, don't take me now, for I am in mid-life;

But You live on through all generations,

You are God.

Your work once formed the earth

When Your own hand designed;

    In the beginning, earth and heaven

        You defined.

Now You remain the same, but heaven and earth will fail;

Our earth will wear out like a garment,

Past its prime.

You will discard it all—

These robes will need a change;

    But You remain the same and Your years Never End.

The children of Your servants flourish in Your home;

Within Your presence all will thrive,

And now, as friends."

PSALM 103

(Of David.)
Tune: Onward Christian Soldiers Marching as to War
"St. Gertrude", Arthur S. Sullivan (1871)

My soul. Who forgives all your misdeeds and sins?

Who heals your diseases and your wounds on Him?

Redeems for good value those who are condemned?

Who crowns you with love and goodness?

Praise Him and commend;

All my inner-being, Praise Him,

Praise His Holy Name.

Praise the LORD, my soul, for

He meets all your needs!

My soul, Whose compassion crowns you in your need,

    Satisfies your longing, Who renews your strength?

That your youthfulness renews like an eagle flies

    Wings so strong and soaring praising,

        Praise the LORD ON HIGH!

            Praise the LORD, my soul, Oh praise Him

            From my inner-being,

            Praise His Holy Name for

            He meets all your needs!

With His benefits He brings hope for the oppressed;

    Hope and justice, He brings, acts of righteousness.

He made known His ways to Moses every day

    So His deeds for His beloved

        Are for us to claim:

            Praise the LORD, my soul, Oh praise Him

            For His benefits!

            Praise His holy Name.

            And make remembrance.

The LORD is compassionate and His love abounds

He will not accuse us though our sins abound!

Slow to anger, He will not harbor or repay

Our intrepid, gross unfairness

To Him, He refrains

From deserved punishment

For He is good always!

Praise the LORD, my soul, Oh,

Praise His Holy Name.

As far as the heights of heaven measure above earth,

His love rises for those trusting in His love;

Far as east horizons measure from the west,

He removes transgressions from us.

Praise the LORD, and bless!

Praise the LORD, my soul, Oh praise Him

From my inner-being,

Praise His Holy Name, for

His benefits and peace.

With a great compassion, He recalls our frame;

   From the dust, He made us; we will wilt in heat.

Flourishing, like flowers do in sweet, grassy fields;

   Yet, the wind blows on the blooms,

      They're gone, and so we yield.

         Their place is forgot without care

         But our LORD loves on

         He's from everlasting,

         And so is His love!

The care of the LORD keeps faithful ones and heirs—

   Righteousness will keep all those who will adhere

Walking in His covenant, following His lead

   They observe His precepts

      And His covenant believe.

         Praise the LORD, my soul, Oh, praise Him;

         From my inner-being,

         Praise His Holy Name for

         He meets all your needs!

The LORD has established His own heavenly throne

From His throne He rules this kingdom for His own.

Angels, you are mighty! Come and praise Your LORD,

All you messengers who work His call

Come join me now!

Praise the LORD, my soul, Oh, praise Him

For His benefits!

Praise His Holy Name.

And make remembrance.

O, praise Him, you heavenly hosts, who dispense His word

Servants who continue in each place of work;

For His fingers are in all, so we praise the LORD!

All you messengers who work His call

Come join me now!

Praise the LORD, my soul, Oh, praise Him

For His benefits!

Praise His Holy Name.

And make remembrance.

PSALM 104

(WATER PSALM)
Tune: I SING THE MIGHTY POWER OF GOD
Isaac Watts (1700) ELLACOMBE (1785)
Alternate: O, LITTLE TOWN OF BETHLEHEM, Ralph
Vaughn Williams altered from Forest Green (1906)

Speak: *Praise the LORD, O my soul.*

O, LORD, Your greatness is a scroll

Protecting like a tent;

You wrap Yourself in honor's robes

In wings of light events!

In garments stretched majestically

Across the heavens fair,

You clothe yourself and dress Your house

With prisms in the air.

Who else can stretch the heavenly mists

In curtains drawing forth?

He lays His upper chamber's beams

In waters of the earth!

Who else can make the clouds His wheels

Of platinum or gold?

Who else can walk on wings of wind,

Who else but God, I'm told!

Who else can make God's angels spring

As spirits to His call?

Or ministers become the flames

Of fires leaping tall?

For You have laid the cornerstones

Of solid earth in space,

That it should never be removed

From gravity's embrace!

You covered earth with waters deep

As with a garment drenched;

Above the mountain heights they stayed.

Rebuked, the seas retrench;

As voices of Your thunder played,

They hastened to their place!

Now, far away they rest in pools

And valleys where they stay.

You've set a cycle, boundary, place
That they may not pass on;
That waters shall not drown the earth
A second time around.
He sends the springs to green the valleys
Flowing down the hills.
They give their drink to every beast
Of every open field.

The wild donkeys quench their thirst
By waters of the earth;
The birds of heaven have their home;
They sing from where they perch.
He pours His water on His hills
From elevation heights;
And moisture flows to satisfy
the earth with grand delights.

He causes grass to grow for herds,

For beef and cattle's cream;

He waters vegetation that

May serve each human being.

He also stores up wine *that* makes

Our hearts and spirits glad,

With water and oil, don't we shine?

With bread our hearts are clad.

The trees of the LORD are full of sap,

Look how these cedars rest!

He planted them in Lebanon,

Where birds now make their nests.

The stork has made her home in the fir; and

The goats in higher hills;

The cliffs are a refuge for the ilk

Of hyrax badger skills.

He ordered the moon for season's crests;

The sun knows when to set.

You make the darkness, and the night,

When creeping beasts are best.

Then, young lions roar after prey,

They seek their food from God.

And with the sun they gather 'round,

And to their dens, they plod.

Now, with the same big rising sun,

Our people go to work;

And to their labors all will toil,

Until the day turns dark.

O, LORD, how manifold Your works!

In wisdom, all are made!

The cycling earth belongs to You,

And seas with teeming things.

All living things, both great and small,

Leviathan at play,

The ships we sail about the world;

These wait for You always.

They hope You give good food to eat,

Their food in season comes.

You give them what they gather in;

Your hand is opened up.

You hide Your face, they scowl in fear;

You take away their breath,

They die and turn from dust to dust,

They finally rest in death.

You send Your Spirit forth to us,

And we are all renewed;

Create new life upon earth's face,

Your spirit like the dew.

May all Your glory, O LORD God,

Endure forevermore;

May You rejoice in all Your work;

May we be answered for.

He looks on earth, and how it quakes;

He touches hills, they smoke.

I choose to sing while I have breath,

To love and not provoke.

I will sing praise to God, my God;

While I have means to sing.

My meditations flow to Him

On all creative streams.

I'm choosing gladness, praising Him.

May You constrict sin's power!

O, choke the wickedness that mocks

Your blessings every hour!

PSALM 105

CROWN HIM WITH MANY CROWNS
DIADEMATA by George J. Elvey (1868)
Alternate Tune: The God of Abrahm, Praise
Thomas Olivers (1772) based on the Jewish hymn, Yigdal
May also be adapted to The Holly and the Ivy

Give to the LORD, your praise!

Proclaim His Name, give thanks;

Make known among the nations,

Say what He has done for you!

Sing to the LORD, en masse;

How wonderful His acts!

We glory in His Holy Name;

Let seekers give Him thanks!

Look to the LORD for strength;

And always seek His face.

Remember all the works and

Wonders He has done for you!

The judgments He pronounced,

For good the earth around,

For you are servants of the LORD,

Of Abraham's renowned.

You are His chosen ones,

He is the Lord our God.

    To Jacob's children,

    He remembers all His promises!

His covenant was laid

    Forever, if a day;

 A thousand generations praise

The covenant He made.

This covenant was shared

To Abraham, and heirs.

    To Isaac, He has sworn an oath,

    To Jacob, He declared—

An everlasting will.

    A covenant decreed:

"To Israel, I will give the land of

Canaan as your deed."

When they were but a few;

In number, they were few.

    As strangers, how they wandered,

    Throughout every foreign land;

One nation to the next,

    The kingdoms they perplexed.

But God let no one touch His own;

    The rulers' aims, He wrecked.

He stated for their good,

"You do not lay a hand

    On my anointed ones,

    And do my prophets no harm."

He called a famine down

    Upon the ruler's land;

Destroying their supply of food,

    For He had made a plan.

God had arranged the way;

His man was sent before.

    A man named Joseph, sold in slavery,

    suffered in this world.

His neck was put in chains;

    His feet had bruises borne.

In shackles, there this Joseph lived,

    God's man betrayed and scorned.

Now all that he foretold—

The word that Joseph brought—

The famine came to pass to show

The LORD was proved in fact.

The king sent for God's man,

    God's man in jail was called.

The king promoted Joseph to be

    Master over all.

Joseph was set in place;

The governor of all.

    Instructing princes as he pleased;

    And elders learned his law.

Then Israel sought his hand;

    They entered Egypt's land.

So, Jacob then resided as a

    Foreigner in Ham.

Then, how the LORD made fruit!

His people thrived and grew,

    Too numerous to ease their host's

    Discomfort for their few.

God turned Egypt to hate

    His people in their gates.

So they conspired against His servants.

    They became enslaved.

He sent another man,

Then two; His chosen ones.

   Moses and Aaron's miracles

   Were signs within the land.

The people, heirs of Ham,

   Saw wonders in the dark;

For had they not rebelled against His word,

   From patriarchs?

Turning their wells to blood,

He caused their fish to die.

   He caused their land to teem with frogs;

   Their air to swarm with flies.

The frogs went up the stairs

   Of rulers, to their beds,

He turned the rain to violent hail,

   With lightning overhead.

Shattering trees and vines,

He struck their figs and wine,

For when He spoke, the locusts came,

And grasshoppers to chyme.

In every field they cleaned;

They ate up every green.

The produce of Egyptian soil

Was fouled, with none to eat.

Then struck the final blow;

The firstborn in their land.

He struck the first fruits of their

Manhood as His reprimand.

Then, Israel followed God,

Sent off with heavy loads;

They took the silver and the gold from

Ham who let them go.

Giving His people clouds,

He spread His welcomed aid.

    He gave a fire in the night

    To give them light for haste.

They asked, and He brought quail.

    He fed them bread of heaven.

He opened up the rock, and water

    Gushed to frantic hands.

These were direct proceeds

Of the LORD's holy pledge

    As given to his servant, Abraham,

    For promised land.

He brought His people out,

    With shouts, rejoicing shouts;

His chosen ones redeemed the lands

    Of nations He denounced.

Servants fell heir to all

That others toiled for—

    That they might keep His precepts,

    And observe His holy laws.

So, praise the LORD, give thanks,

    And enter to your land.

For you are heirs of promises

    The LORD has freely given.

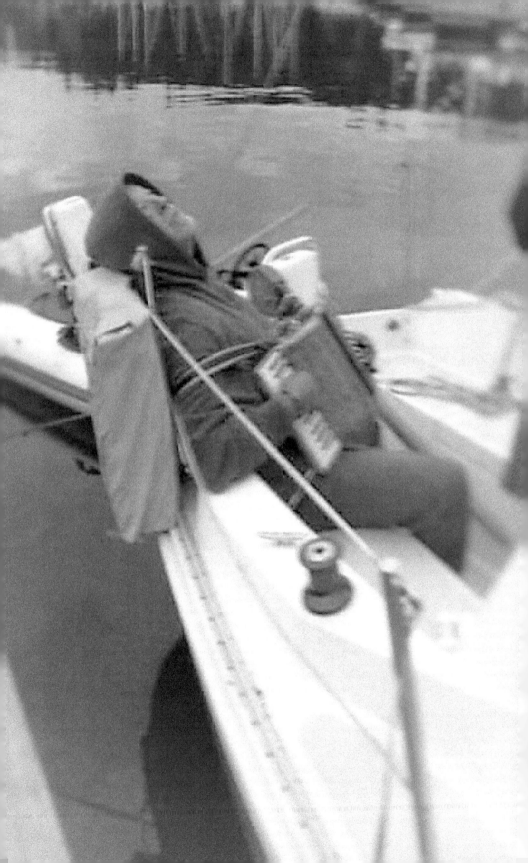

PSALM 106

TUNE: O WORSHIP THE KING
Sir Robert Grant (1812)

Give praise to the LORD; His unfailing love!

Give thanks to the LORD; for His goodness we trust!

Now, who can proclaim all the wonders of God?

Or fully declare every praise of the LORD?

He blesses His own, the just who do right;

How happy their lives and their future is bright.

Remember me, LORD, when You favor Your own,

And come to my aid when You save those You know.

That I may enjoy a prosperity.

I see they all share in the happiness You bring.

To Your chosen ones of Your nation's delight;

I'll join Your inheritance praising Your might.

I know we have sinned, our ancestors did;
   We mimic their wrongs, as the wicked of wit.
Our ancestors passing through Egypt forgot
   Your wonders and light, giving no second thought.

They did not recall His kind, guiding hand,
   And at the Red Sea, they began to demand.
Yet He saved them for His Name's sake in the end,
   Despite how they cursed Him, He rescued again.

He walled up the sea and dried up the reeds;
   He led them through sea basins, dry to proceed.
From Egypt's stampede, how He saved and prevailed,
   By sinking those chariots, in waves as they trailed.

The waters surpassed, and Egypt was lost;
   Their champions went down, with their means to accost.
Then Israel delighted the lost retinue;
   They sang out His praise for God's promise was true!

But soon they forgot what YAHWEH had done,
   And they did not wait for His Sovereignty to run.
They fostered their cravings, let each manifest;
   In their wilderness, they put God to the test.

So, He gave them what they each clambered for,
    But He sent a wasting disease that they bore.
Then burgeoned an envy through Israelite camps,
    At Moses and Aaron in God's good command.

The earth opened up, it swallowed Dathan;
    It buried the cohorts of errant Abiram.
A fire blazed over conspirators of blame,
    Consuming the wicked and, with them, their aims.

At Horeb, the tribes constructed a calf,
    And worshipped the idol of metal they had cast.
Exchanging their glorious God for a bull,
    A calf that eats grass, how they acted as fools!

How could they forget the God who had saved,
    Or His miracles while in Egypt's enclave?
His acts, they denied as His rescuing hand
    From slavery and from the Red Sea's deadly sands.

So YAHWEH gave word to kill those arrayed —
    Had Moses, His chosen, not stood up and prayed.
He stood by himself in the breach of God's path,
    To stay God's destruction of Israel by wrath.

Then at pleasant doors, reviling their land;

    They did not believe God's own promise would stand.

They grumbled in their tents and did not obey,

    So God swore with uplifted hand to their days.

He swore He would cause their death in the wild,

    Abandon their children to other nations' guile.

The LORD said He'd scatter them throughout the earth;

    He counted their promised land as a still-birth.

They yoked the twelve tribes to the Baal of Peor,

    And ate sacrifices left over from these gods.

These gods without mouths, without life, without power,

    So, Israel enflamed the LORD'S hand and His dour.

A plague of demise broke out in their midst,

    But Phinehas stood up interceding for them;

The credit was his when the ravages broke,

    For his righteous act made atonement their cloak.

At Meribah's pools, they angered the LORD,

    And troubling Moses, they whined and they roared.

They prodded against the good Servant of God,

    and rash were the words from his lips like a sword.

They did not destroy the dwellers on lands
   They conquered, and did not obey God's command.
They mingled, instead, with these nations at ease,
   Adopted their customs and idol deities.

Then strange fetishes ensnared their applause;
   Their children they sacrificed to these false gods.
The innocent blood of their daughters and sons,
   They shed as they sacrificed to Canaan's own.

By spilling their blood, the land was defiled.
   Defiling themselves, by their shedding of blood;
The slippery slope of their arrogant souls,
   Made holy souls prostitutes, angering the LORD.

The LORD then abhorred His people gone rogue;
   His inheritance was now bitter to revoke.
He gave them to enemy nations to purge;
   His people were ruled by their foes as a scourge.

Yet, count all the times the LORD rescued them,

    And still they were twisted as rebels in sin.

They wasted away, yet He saw their distress,

    When He heard their cry, YAHWEH saved the oppressed.

For their sake, His covenant He invoked,

    Then guards showed them mercy to lighten their load.

LORD, save us, our God, gather us from the earth,

    That taught, we may thank You, rejoicing in mirth.

When we see Your glory, we'll praise Your Name,

    And shout hallelujah for merciful acclaims.

Forever and lasting, the people will say,

    "Amen! Praise the LORD, hallelujah, YAHWEH!

The Ten Commandments

Exodus 20 (NIV)

And God spoke all these words:

[2] "I am the LORD your God, who brought you out of Egypt, out of the land of slavery.

[3] "You shall have no other gods besides me.

[4] "You shall not make for yourself an image in the form of anything in heaven above or on the earth beneath or in the waters below. [5] You shall not bow down to them or worship them; for I, the LORD your God, am a jealous God, punishing the children for the sin of the parents to the third and fourth generation of those who hate me, [6] but showing love to a thousand generations of those who love me and keep My commandments.

[7] "You shall not misuse the name of the LORD your God, for the LORD will not hold anyone guiltless who misuses His name.

[8] "Remember the Sabbath day by keeping it holy. [9] Six days you shall labor and do all your work, [10] but the seventh day is a sabbath to the LORD your God. On it you shall not do any work, neither you, nor your son or daughter, nor your male or female servant, nor your animals, nor any foreigner residing in your towns.

[11] For in six days the LORD made the heavens and the earth, the sea, and all that is in them, but He rested on the seventh day. Therefore the LORD blessed the Sabbath day and made it holy.

[12] "Honor your father and your mother, so that you may live long in the land the LORD your God is giving you.

[13] "You shall not murder.

[14] "You shall not commit adultery.

[15] "You shall not steal.

[16] "You shall not give false testimony against your neighbor.

[17] "You shall not covet your neighbor's house. You shall not covet your neighbor's wife, or his male or female servant, his ox or donkey, or anything that belongs to your neighbor."

CAPTUREMEBOOKS

Go to: https://www.CaptureMeBooks.com
for our other book selections

Interact with us!
https://www.facebook.com/PsalmHymns.Larkins/?ref=bookmarks
Or
Singing The Psalms! (FaceBook group)

Please feel free to connect with us on Facebook at **Psalm-Hymns Singable Psalms**

Order other products:

www.CaptureBookstore.com

CPSIA information can be obtained
at www.ICGtesting.com
Printed in the USA
LVHW080454080620
657648LV00022B/2504

9 781732 445772